The Town Mouse and the Country Mouse

Retold by Sue Arengo
Illustrated by Kate Aldous

OXFORD

UNIVERSITY PRESS

Before you read, can you match the words with the pictures?

1 Town Mouse

2 Country Mouse

3 bed

4 cow

5 home

6 cart

7 food

a

b

c

d

e

f

g

THIS is Country Mouse's home. One day his friend, Town Mouse, comes to see him. 'Hello, Country Mouse!' says Town Mouse. 'Hello, my friend!' says Country Mouse.

country   mouse   town

There's a lot to eat. But Town Mouse
thinks the food is strange.
He doesn't like it very much.
So he only eats a little bit.
'Please have some more,' says
Country Mouse.
'It's very nice,' says Town Mouse,
'but no thank you.'

Country Mouse gives Town Mouse his bed.
'You can have my bed tonight,' he says.
'Thank you,' says Town Mouse.

But Country Mouse's bed is strange.
Town Mouse doesn't like it very much.
He can't go to sleep.
It's very dark and quiet.

---

bed

In the morning Town Mouse is tired.
But Country Mouse isn't tired.
'Come on!' he says.
'Let's go and get some food.'

The grass is long and wet.
Town Mouse's feet and trousers are wet.
He doesn't like the country very much!

It's only a cow!

There's a cow in the field.
'Oh!' cries Town Mouse 'What's that?'
'It's only a cow!' laughs Country Mouse.

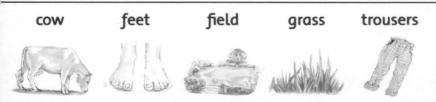

| cow | feet | field | grass | trousers |

What do they say?

1 __e__

2 ___

3 ___

4 ___

5 ___

a Let's go and get some food.

b You can have my bed tonight.

c It's only a cow!

d It's very nice, but no thank you.

e Hello, my friend!

Fill in the gaps.

~~in~~   to   at   in   in   in

Country Mouse lives
___in___ the country.

Town Mouse sleeps
_____ his bed.

Town Mouse can't
go _____ sleep.

There's a cow
_____ the field.

It's dark_____
night in the country.

'Do you like the country?' asks
Country Mouse.
'It's very strange here,' says Town
Mouse. 'It's very interesting.
It's different.
But I think I like the town best.'

'Life is good in the country,' says Country Mouse.
'Yes,' says Town Mouse. 'But I like the town better.
It's nice and warm and dry in the town.
It isn't dark at night and there's a lot to see.
It's very interesting.
And the food! Oh, there's a lot of food! Let's go
there. Come with me and see.'

The next day the two mice see a cart.
It's going to town.
'Hurry up you sheep!' says the man.
'I want to go to town.'
'Listen,' says Town Mouse. 'That cart's
going to town. Come on.'

sheep

It's good to be home again.

Soon Town Mouse is home.
'Ah!' he says, happily. 'It's good to be home again.'
But Country Mouse thinks:
'What a lot of noise!
What a lot of people!'

home

Answer the questions.

1 Town Mouse sleeps in Country Mouse's ...
   a ☐ garden   b ☑ bed   c ☐ field

2 It's very ... in the country at night.
   a ☐ noisy   b ☐ quiet   c ☐ dry

3 In the morning, Town Mouse is ...
   a ☐ tired   b ☐ warm   c ☐ happy

4 They get some food in a ...
   a ☐ shop   b ☐ field   c ☐ house

5 The grass is long and ...
   a ☐ blue   b ☐ dry   c ☐ wet

6 Town Mouse wants to go back to ...
   a ☐ the country   b ☐ the town   c ☐ the sea

7 The two mice go to town ...
   a ☐ on a cart   b ☐ in a car   c ☐ on a bus

What's this?

1 Is this the country?___No.___
   Is it quiet here? _____

2 Is this a house?_____
   Is it small? _____
   Does Country Mouse like it? _____

3 Is this a cow? _____

4 Who's this?_____
   Is he happy?_____
   Does he like it here? _____

The house is very big.
Country Mouse doesn't like it very much.

Oh! What's that?

It's only the clock.

Suddenly there's a strange noise.
'Oh! What's that?' he says.
'It's only the clock,' laughs Town Mouse.
'Look! I live there. Let's go and eat. Come on!'

clock

There's a lot to eat. But Country Mouse
thinks the food is strange.
He doesn't like it very much.
So he only eats a little bit.
'Please have some more,' says Town Mouse.
'It's very nice,' says Country Mouse,
'but no thank you.'

Town Mouse gives Country Mouse his bed.
'You can have my bed tonight,' he says.
'Thank you,' says Country Mouse.

But Town Mouse's bed is strange.
Country Mouse doesn't like it very much.
He can't go to sleep.
It isn't dark in the room and the street
is very noisy.

street

In the morning Country Mouse is tired.
But Town Mouse isn't tired.
'Come on!' he says. 'Let's go and get some food.'

But there's a cat and they can't go out.

Write the words.

clock food ~~mice~~ people

sheep street tired

_ _ _ _

m i c e

<u>m</u> <u>i</u> <u>c</u> <u>e</u>

_ _ _ _ _

_ _ _ _ _ _

_ _ _ _ _ _

_ _ _ _ _

Put the words in the correct order.

1 gives   Mouse   Town   bed   him   his   .

Town Mouse gives him his bed.

2 Mouse's   Town   is   strange   bed   .

_____

3 noisy   is   street   The   very   .

_____

4 go   Country   can't   to   Mouse   sleep   .

_____

5 morning   the   In   tired   Mouse
  Country   is   .

_____

6 Mouse   strange   Country   thinks   is   food
  the   .

_____

At last the cat goes away.
The two mice are very hungry.

STOP! It's a trap!

Suddenly, Country Mouse sees
something.
'Look!' he shouts. 'Cheese!'
'STOP!' shouts Town Mouse.
'Don't touch that! It's a trap!'

cheese   trap

Do you like the town?' asks Town Mouse.
'It's very strange here,' says Country Mouse.
'It's interesting. It's different.
But I think I like the country best.'

'Life is good in the town,' says Town Mouse.
'Yes,' says Country Mouse. 'But I like
the country better.
It's nice and quiet in the country.'
'I understand,' says Town Mouse.
'We like different things.'

The next day they see a cart. It's going to the country.

'Hurry up you children,' says the driver.

'I want to go to the country.'

'Listen,' says Country Mouse.

'That cart's going to the country.

Goodbye my friend. Thank you.'

'Write to me,' says Town Mouse.

Soon Country Mouse is home.
He's in the country.
He sits by the fire.
'Ah!' he says happily. 'It's good to be
home again.'

fire

Answer the questions.

1 Who can't go to sleep in the dark?

a ☐ Country Mouse   c ☐ the cat

b ☑ Town Mouse

2 What is long and wet?

a ☐ the cow   b ☐ the food   c ☐ the grass

3 Where is it warm and dry?

a ☐ in the field   c ☐ in the town

b ☐ in the country

4 What makes a strange noise at five o'clock?

a ☐ the cat   b ☐ the trap   c ☐ the clock

5 There's a ... so the mice can't go out.

a ☐ cat   b ☐ trap   c ☐ dog

6 What is in the trap?

a ☐ a mouse   b ☐ a cat   c ☐ some cheese

7 Country Mouse is happy ...

a ☐ by the fire   b ☐ in the town   c ☐ on the cart

Crossword.

bed · cart · cheese · clock · cow · grass · mouse · sheep · trousers · trap

Act the play.

Scene 1

Chant	Town Mouse comes to the country. He comes to see his friend, Country Mouse.
Town Mouse	Hello, Country Mouse!
Country Mouse	Hello, my friend!

Scene 2

Country Mouse	Have some food.
Town Mouse	Only a little, thank you.
Chant	Town Mouse thinks the food is strange. He doesn't like it very much.
Country Mouse	Please, have some more.
Town Mouse	It's very nice, but no thank you.

Scene 3

Country Mouse	Come on, come on!
Town Mouse	Where are we going?
Country Mouse	To get some food.
Chant	There's a cow in the field.
Town Mouse	Oh! What's that?
Country Mouse	It's only a cow!

27

Scene 4

Country Mouse   Life is good in the country.

Town Mouse   Yes, but I like the town better. It's
                    nice and warm and dry in the town. It
                    isn't dark at night and there's a lot to
                    see. Let's go to the town.

Scene 5

Town Mouse   Ah! It's good to be home again.

Country Mouse   What a lot of noise! What a lot of
                    people! What a big house!

Chant   Tick-tock, tick-tock, tick-tock ...
                    Ding, ding, ding, ding, ding!

Country Mouse   Oh! What's that?

Town Mouse   It's only the clock. Look! I live there.
                    Let's go and eat. Come on!

Scene 6

Town Mouse   Have some food.

Country Mouse   Only a little, thank you.

Chant   Country Mouse thinks the food is
                    strange. He doesn't like it very much.

Scene 7

Town Mouse	Come on! Let's go and get some food.
Country Mouse	Oh! What's that?
Town Mouse	It's a cat. Stop! Don't go out!
Chant	At last the cat goes away.
Country Mouse	Look! Cheese!
Town Mouse	Stop! Don't touch that! It's a trap!

Scene 8

Town Mouse	Life is good in the town.
Country Mouse	Yes, but I like the country better. It's nice and quiet in the country.
Town Mouse	I understand. We like different things.
Country Mouse	Goodbye my friend. Thank you.
Town Mouse	Goodbye. Write to me!
Country Mouse	Ah! It's good to be home again.
Chant	It's good to be home in the country. And it's good to be home in the town.

OXFORD
UNIVERSITY PRESS

Great Clarendon Street, Oxford OX2 6DP

Oxford University Press is a department of the University of Oxford.
It furthers the University's objective of excellence in research, scholarship,
and education by publishing worldwide in

Oxford New York

Auckland Cape Town Dar es Salaam Hong Kong Karachi
Kuala Lumpur Madrid Melbourne Mexico City Nairobi
New Delhi Shanghai Taipei Toronto

With offices in

Argentina Austria Brazil Chile Czech Republic France Greece
Guatemala Hungary Italy Japan Poland Portugal Singapore
South Korea Switzerland Thailand Turkey Ukraine Vietnam

OXFORD and OXFORD ENGLISH are registered trade marks of
Oxford University Press in the UK and in certain other countries

سرشناسه :	: أرنگو، سو Arengo, Sue
عنوان و نام پدیدآور :	The town mouse and the country mouse/ retold by Sue Arengo. ; illustrated by Kate Aldouse.
مشخصات نشر :	: تهران : نشر ابداع، ۱۳۹۱= ۲۰۱۲م.
مشخصات ظاهری :	: ۳۲ ص.مصور (رنگی).
فروست :	Family and friends; 2 :
وضعیت فهرست نویسی :	: فیپا
یادداشت :	: انگلیسی.
یادداشت :	: افست از روی چاپ ۲۰۰۹م.:oxford university press.
آوانویسی عنوان :	: تاون ماوس ...
موضوع :	: زبان انگلیسی -- راهنمای آموزشی (ابتدایی)
شناسه افزوده :	: آلدوس، کیت، تصویرگر
شناسه افزوده :	Aldous, Kate :
رده بندی کنگره :	PE۱۰۶۵/۱۳۷ت۲ ۱۳۹۱ :
رده بندی دیویی :	۴۲۸/۲ :
شماره کتابشناسی ملی :	۲۹۹۵۴۱۹ :

The Town Mouse
and the Country
Mouse

ناشر : ابداع - زبان مهر

تیراژ : ۵۰۰۰ جلد

۱۰

لیتوگرافی : ندا   چاپ : فرشیوه
مرکز پخش : انتشارات زبان مهر
۶۶۴۹۴۰۰۰ -۶۶۴۹۵۰۰۰-۶۶۴۹۶۰۰۰